Eagle Eyes

A CHILD'S VIEW OF ATTENTION DEFICIT DISORDER

BY JEANNE GEHRET, M.A.

Illustrations and design by Susan Covert
Foreword by Michael Gordon, Ph.D.

Many thanks to those who reviewed and consulted on this book:

Cheryl Guenther, Parent, The Norman Howard School, New York
Corinne Olson, Student, New York
Harvey Parker, Ph.D., Founder of Children with Attention Deficit Disorders (CH.A.D.D.), Florida
Jon Price, M.D., F.A.A.P., Pediatrician, Ohio
Peg Schoenfeld, Special education teacher, New York
John F. Taylor, Ph.D., Family psychologist, Oregon

Special thanks to **Judy Olson,** board member of the Greater Rochester Attention Deficit Disorder Association (GRADDA), who asked for *Eagle Eyes* to be written; and to the naturalists at the Cumming Nature Center of the Rochester Museum and Science Center.

ISBN 0-9625136-1-X
© copyright 1991 Jeanne Gehret
© copyright illustrations 1991 Susan Covert

 Verbal Images Press

19 Fox Hill Drive
Fairport, New York 14450
(716) 377-3807 • Fax: (716) 377-5401

Note to parents and teachers

Over the following pages you will read a delightful story about a boy who shows common signs of an Attention Deficit Disorder (ADD). His name is Ben and he seems to find himself struggling in situations that require him to concentrate and to control his behavior.

Ben's attentional problems cause him to scatter seed on the trail, fail to notice others' feelings, and forget to turn in the homework assignments he toiled over. He annoys his sister with his exhuberance and clumsiness. His impulsiveness gets him in trouble, and the frequent punishments that ensue convince him that he's bad.

Despite his problems, Ben has many strengths, not the least of which are his enthusiasm and desire to please. His parents and Dr. Lawson help him channel his energies and find strategies for coping. So successful are these efforts that he helps his father when an emergency arises.

Through Ben's adventures, parents can teach their children to confront their vulnerabilities with an air of acceptance and a problem-solving attitide. The Morning Song and the Feelings Game are two fun ways to begin. Teachers can easily modify these techniques for classroom use.

Those of us involved in the evaluation and treatment of this disorder quickly come to appreciate the potential so many ADD children have for transforming their weaknesses to strengths. Controlling the ADD symptoms can often allow their more lovable and productive qualities to emerge.

Learn and enjoy!

Michael Gordon, Ph.D.
SUNY Health Science Center at Syracuse
Professor of Psychiatry
Director, Attention Deficit Hyperactivity
Disorders Clinic

When my family goes to Birdsong Trail, I spot more wildlife than anybody else. Our last couple trips there didn't go so well, though. Here's what happened.

We took birdseed because the chickadees are so tame that they eat right out of people's hands. As soon as I saw the hungry gray birds, I dropped some food on the path. "Ben, stop it," Emily snapped. "If you drop it on the path they won't eat out of our hands." Why didn't I think of that?

As we hiked along the snowy path near the pond, my eyes followed a chickadee to the top of an oak. I spied a clump of leaves and sticks — a nest? An eagle circled high overhead. Suddenly it swooped down into the water and grabbed a fish.

I ran on ahead to where Emily was feeding chickadees. "Emily, guess what," I panted. "I saw an eagle's nest and..." In my haste I tripped, scattering seed on the path. The chickadees flew away from my sister and gathered at my feet, eating greedily.

"You klutz!" she cried. "Can't you ever be quiet? You scared the birds away from me...and now they're all eating at your feet!"

Crying, she turned to Mom and Dad. "I can't have any fun when Ben's around. He's such a pain!" I threw some snow at her.

"Ben, stop!" Mom said. "Would you please be more careful not to scare the birds? Come on, Emily; we'll find other chickadees around the bend."

A pain, I thought—that's me. Always ruining things, making people mad. I stayed behind, thinking, *They're better off without me.*

I walked so slowly that I must have examined every inch of that trail—the bird feeder where cardinals feast, the deer footprints by the bridge, the signpost with the eagle painted on it. I wanted to tell Emily what I saw, but she was still mad. She glared at me all the way home.

After supper Mom said, "Time for homework, kids. Go get your folders and let's see what you have to do."

Emily spoke up quickly. "I don't have any. I finished mine in school on Friday."

"Good job, honey. How about you, Ben?"

"I don't have any either," I replied. But a few minutes later she returned holding a note from my folder. Frowning, she read, "Benjamin has not done his homework for two days. Please have him complete pages 67-75 of these worksheets."

So I had to sit and work the rest of the evening while Emily got to rearrange her fish tank. I was so angry I couldn't fall asleep until midnight.

"Pass your homework in, class," my teacher said the next morning. I smiled to myself, glad that I had mine in my folder for a change. But no, my folder was empty! After all that work!

Shortly after that, Dad took me to see Dr. Lawson. She told me I have Attention Deficit Disorder, which is often called ADD for short. ADD means that my body doesn't have enough of the chemicals that help me control how I move and think. I forget to take my homework to school because my thoughts run ahead of me. That's why I bump into things, too. And all that energy keeps me awake into the night.

All this time I thought I was nothing but a clumsy, bad kid. Huh!

Dad explained that I have eagle eyes; I notice every-thing. But eagles know when to stop looking around and zoom in on their prey. Me, I just keep noticing more things and miss my catch.

Dr. Lawson showed Dad and me some tricks so I can pay attention to what's important. That night we made up a song about getting ready for school so I'll have everything I need. Here's how it goes:

The Morning Song

adapted from the traditional tune "Oats, peas, beans, and barley"

1. Clothes, hair, shoes, and backpack, lunch, Clothes, hair, shoes and
2. Clear the ta- ble wash my face, Get my coat and

1. backpack, lunch, Clothes, hair, shoes and backpack, lunch, That is what I do.
2. get my boots, Grab my backpack, give a kiss, That is what I do.

When I sing "backpack," I know it's time to put my homework in my backpack. Since I've started singing the Morning Song, I haven't forgotten any of my school things.

Another thing I like is the soft music that Mom gave me to help me relax at night. It quiets the thoughts that run around inside my head. Dr. Lawson prescribed medicine that gives my body more of the chemicals it needs.

Dr. Lawson also taught us to play the Feelings Game. Dad makes a face like he's angry, or sad, or pleased, and I guess how he's feeling by reading his face and body. One day, when I was crayoning on Emily's homework, I noticed that her face looked like Daddy's does when he's mad. I stopped right away and she didn't go crying to Mom like she usually does.

Since we've been doing the things Dr. Lawson suggested, I feel better. And I don't feel like I'm such a pain in the neck. In fact, people even seem glad to have me around.

This spring, when Dad and Emily and I returned to Birdsong Trail, I took binoculars to watch for eagles. Instead, I spied a pair of ducks in the stream.

A thunderstorm sent us dashing back toward the car. Just as we were rounding the bend by the bird feeder, thunder clapped and lightning nearly blinded us. Dad tripped over a rock and twisted his knee.

His face wrinkled with pain. "Emily, you're the oldest," he said. "Will you follow the trail back to the ranger station and get help?" She looked scared. "I don't know the way...." she began.

"I can find it, Dad!" I interrupted. "After you pass the old gate, you follow this trail till you cross the creek and turn at the signpost with the eagle on it. It's not far to the ranger station after that."

"Ben, I knew those eagle eyes of yours would come in handy," Dad replied. "You'll find the way just fine. Emily can stay here to keep me company."

As I turned to go, Dad called, "Hurry, Ben! I need you."

Swift as an eagle, I zoomed off toward the ranger station and got help for Dad. I was the only one who could do it.

And that's when I realized it's good to be me.

Works by Jeanne Gehret

Eagle Eyes: A Child's View of Attention Deficit Disorder, 1991. Ages 6 to 10. 32-page picture book with foreword by Michael Gordon, Ph.D. $7.95

Learning Disabilities and The Don't-give-up Kid, 1990. Ages 6 to 9. 32-page picture book with note to parents by the Association for the Learning Disabled and glossary. $7.95

"The Struggle to Learn," 1989. In-depth magazine story, unbound; three in-depth profiles of the struggle to obtain services for three adolescents with learning disabilities and ADD. $2.00 (free shipping when ordered with book)

Please enclose check with order. No purchase orders on fewer than three items. Normal delivery 3 weeks.*

Quantity	Call for information on quantity discounts.	Amount
	Title	
	Eagle Eyes @ $7.95	
	Learning Disabilities and The Don't-give-up Kid @ $7.95	
	The Struggle to Learn @ $2.00	
	Subtotal	
	New York residents, please add 7% sales tax	
	Shipping: $1.70 for the first book and 40 cents for each additional book. $1.00 for "The Struggle to Learn" (Free shipping with book.) *(If you wish express shipping, add $3.00 to above charges.)	
	Total	

 Verbal Images Press

19 Fox Hill Drive
Fairport, New York 14450
(716) 377-3807 Fax: (716) 377-5401